M000118973

{21 Days}

A Spiritually Healthy Life

Realize Your Goal to
Create a More Spiritually Healthy Life

Jeff Suhr received a degree in history from UC San Diego. He then went on to receive his Masters of Divinity from Westminster Seminary California, after which he was ordained as a pastor in the Presbyterian Church of America. Jeff has been serving as pastor of New Life Mission Church in Orange County, California, for the past six years.

Jeff and his wife Helen Suhr are happily married with three beautiful children, and have both been Christians since high school. Since then, the Lord has taken them on a spiritual journey via various overseas mission trips, church planting experiences, and ministering to God's people. God has challenged both of them to be equipped with biblical truth in order to counsel, teach, and comfort His people.

© Orange Circle Studio Corporation
Written by Jeff Suhr with Helen Suhr

All rights reserved.
No part of this book may be reproduced in any form
without written permission from the publisher.

A division of Orange Circle Studio

Irvine, CA 92618
PH: 949-727-0800
StudioOh.com

ISBN 978-1-60897-234-0

Printed in China

"There is a God shaped vacuum in the heart of every man which cannot be filled by any created thing, but only by God, the Creator, made known through Jesus."

—Blaise Pascal

Chances are, you bought this journal because you desire spiritual renewal, revival, and refreshment. You want to grow spiritually and strengthen your relationship with God. The goal of this journal is to help you develop an intimate union with our Lord Jesus Christ by establishing a habit of spending time with God. Using practical step by step guidelines, this journal will support you in creating a plan to launch habits for a life that is more focused on Christ.

We all have habits, and most habits are bad habits that we try to break. What if we could create a habit that would help us to draw closer to the Lord? By developing habits that remind us to, "...seek first the kingdom of God and his righteousness" (Matthew 6:33), it's very possible to live a more Christ-centered life. Many people exhaust much time and effort in their attempts to develop habits that benefit their earthly lives—diet, exercise, spending/saving, personal grooming. Such practices have their benefits and are valuable. But how much more time and effort should be put into cultivating habits that would promote our spiritual lives? With a *daily* focus on Christ, we are reminded that worldly needs and desires are less important than how closely we are walking with the Lord.

MAKE IT A HABIT IN 21 DAYS

Most of us have made New Year's resolutions, only to break them before January is over. The reality is, learning new habits, introducing a new behavior, or replacing old habits is not easily accomplished. Interestingly, research reveals that it is more effective to create change by introducing rituals instead of focusing on self-discipline as a means to change.

Studies have shown that it takes approximately 21 days to transition old memory patterns into new ones. In other words, if you do an act consistently for 21 days it will become second nature—a habit. Using this journal consistently for 21 days will help you begin a pattern in your living that points you to Christ and the blessings of His grace. By practicing a daily habit of seeking and appreciating God's grace through spiritual disciplines, our desire is that God would *cultivate your soul.*

Realistically, having good religious habits does not **guarantee** a thriving Christian life. But faithful spiritual disciplines like Bible reading, prayer, and journaling are a means that God uses to keep us focused on Him. They are daily reminders that "...man does not live by bread alone, but man lives by every word that comes from the mouth of the Lord" (Deuteronomy 8:3). Ultimately, we have to remember that God uses our efforts to help us grow in our faith, but He doesn't grow us *because* of our efforts. This journal will support you in identifying and establishing habits that will lead to a more Christ-centered life. A life that **God** can transform and be the center of.

THE NEED TO SPEND TIME WITH GOD

Committing yourself for 21 days, no matter how noble the motivation, may seem a bit daunting. The only reason anyone would want to commit to a task for any amount of time would be to reap benefits that outweigh the cost. In regards to our spiritual lives, it is easy to confess the depth of our need for God's presence in our lives. Simply put, we can't live this life by our own strength, according to our own wisdom. Life is just too hard. We need God and we need Him every day.

We live in an increasingly fast-paced world where demands at school, work, and family weigh heavily upon us. Millions of Americans find themselves paralyzed by mounting bills, fear of layoffs, and rising mortgage payments. What's more, due to technological advancements in communication, we're constantly bombarded with phone calls, voice-mails, e-mails, and text messages. We are invaded by rings, pings, and dings. The endless electronic assault chokes out any time to "be still and know that He is God" (Psalm 46:10). We need to be spiritually anchored in the promises of Scripture. A life that puts Christ as the focus is the best way to have hope each day.

In order to mature (or even survive) spiritually we **need** to *set aside time for God each and every day*. We **need** to be proactive. We **need** to make God a priority. Just like eating meals, bathing, and brushing our teeth, spending time with God needs to become a part of our everyday life.

When our lives are centered on Christ, when we are walking with Him every day, we can experience the calming influence and peace of our Lord Jesus Christ. Remember Jesus' miracle when He silenced the raging sea? Though the winds blew and the waves crashed, though the seaworthy disciples were frightened and panicked, Jesus alone stood calm. He exuded confidence without doubt, and cried out, "Peace! Be still!" (Mark 4:39), and the raging sea immediately became still. Jesus desires to have the same effect on your life. A busy life does not necessitate a busy heart. As we spend time with God, our spiritual lives fall in order, and we can experience peace, even in the midst of life's storms. Our hearts can be quiet and free from strife. It's time to make a change; join with me in committing the next 21 days fully to the Lord! It's time to put God back where He belongs—at the center of your life.

HOW TO USE THIS JOURNAL

This journal is a tool to help you work through the necessary steps toward achieving your goal. It will prove most effective if it is used daily to reflect and record your thoughts.

After following your 21 day schedule, fill in the corresponding forms. You'll also find lined pages where you can reflect on your reading, and write your thoughts, feelings, and prayers. Find detailed explanations on how to use this journal on pages 7 – 9.

People who journal in an effort to attain a goal are more likely to succeed. Why? Journaling enables you to work through your thoughts and emotions in a methodical way. It also allows you to handle problems privately with God, without interference from others. Writing it all down provides insight into who God is, your relationship with Him, and how these two things should guide you in your thoughts, emotions, and living. Just the physical act of *writing* incites thought. It keeps you focused, alert, and sensitive to what the Holy Spirit is trying to teach you.

This journal also comes with a wristband, which will serve as a constant reminder of your goal and the steps needed to achieve it. Wear it every day during the 21 days.

"A goal without a plan is just a wish."

—Antoine de Saint-Exupéry

A good plan must be set in place in order to achieve your goal, and your success is greatly dependent upon the quality of your plan. I have seen many fired-up Christians vow to spend more time with God, only to see them lose steam after a few days. Usually, the culprit is unreasonable expectations and goals. They had the right heart but the wrong plan. Going solely by emotions or heartfelt promises to the Lord is not enough to combat our weaknesses and sin. We need concrete steps for how we will attain our sincere desire to grow closer to Christ.

One decision you will need to make is **when** you will meet with the Lord. Since research indicates that habits form after repeating an activity for 21 *consecutive* days, it is crucial that you set aside a time that makes this possible. Don't set yourself up for failure by choosing a time that conflicts with your schedule on Tuesdays and Thursdays, or a time that is highly susceptible to interruptions. Every person's situation is different. Determine what time works best for you and make it a fixed part of your schedule. Keep in mind that the early morning works best for many Christians and can set the tone for the day.

The next factor to consider is **where** you will meet with the Lord. Fortunately, one of the distinctives of the Christian faith is that God can be met *anywhere*—in your closet, in your car, in your office, or even at a coffee shop. Ideally, you want to choose a place with minimal distractions. Wherever it is, make sure you are alone with God and able to focus.

How long should your times be with the Lord? I recommend that you start off small, say five to ten minutes in the beginning. As you deepen your relationship with Him, it will become natural for you to want to spend longer times with Him. For now, the focus should be on **consistency** rather than quantity. As consistency grows, you will discover that the quantity and quality of your meetings will also develop.

When: I will spend time with God every day at ___6___ (am)/pm.

Where: I will meet God in ___My Car___.

How long?: I will meet Him for at least ___10___ minutes.

6

PART 1—BIBLE READING

Now that your plan is set in place, it's time to discuss what you will be doing during your times with God. Simply put, you will be dialoguing with God, which entails both listening and speaking. We listen to God by reading His Word, and He communicates to us through His holy Scriptures. The Bible is not a textbook nor is it a theological encyclopedia. It is the Living Word and through His Word God saves us, teaches us, rebukes us, corrects us, and trains us in all righteousness (2 Timothy 3:16). In it is everything we need to be thoroughly equipped for every good work.

To start out, begin with the Gospel of John. In my opinion, it is the most easily understood of the Gospels because it helps us to grasp the significance of Jesus' life, death, and resurrection. I recommend reading one section at a time.

Most Bibles separate sections with sub-headings. For example, my Bible divides John 2 into three sections: *The Wedding at Cana, Jesus Cleanses the Temple,* and *Jesus Knows What Is in Man.* John 2 would then be read over a course of three days.

In addition, reading through an entire book of the Bible is more preferable than spontaneously jumping around from place to place. This keeps you from having to decide what to read every day and enables you to quickly pick up where you last left off. After you complete a book, choose a book that is short in length (think more along the lines of Ephesians, rather than Deuteronomy). This is so that, in case you find yourself dragging your feet in the middle of a book, you know that the next book is right around the corner.

How you absorb the Bible is very important. Your reading should include three components.

1. Summarize—In your journal, jot down summary notes of what you've read. Record the basic facts of what happened and what was said; try not to analyze it at this point. This is important because we want to ensure that we properly understand what the Bible says before we apply it to our lives. Often, misapplication begins with misunderstanding.

2. Meditate—Meditate on the facts. Allow the Scriptures to "marinate" in your mind. Just as food often tastes best after it has marinated in its own juices, so, too, the Scriptures are often best digested when we allow them to simmer and sit in our thoughts. During this time, ask yourself the following reflective questions: *What does this teach me about God? What does God want me to learn about me? Is there a specific sin that I need to repent of? How does this passage testify of who Jesus Christ is and what He has done?*

3. Respond—Now is the time to take what you've learned and bring it to the Lord through prayer. If God's Word revealed a specific sin in your life that needs to be confessed, then confess it. If God's Word caused you to appreciate God for who He is or what He has done, then praise Him. If God's Word led you to desire to change in one way or another, write down specifically how you want to change. This response portion is a healthy reminder that true theology (the study of God) leads to doxology (glory to God). That is, knowing His Word impacts us holistically—our minds, our hearts, and our wills and actions.

PART 2—PRAYING

If God speaks to us through His Word, we speak to Him through prayer. Prayer is the heartbeat of the Christian life. As Martin Luther once said, "To be a Christian without prayer is no more possible than to be alive without breathing." The vitality of our relationship with God is dependent as much on prayer as it is on reading God's Word. We need to learn how to pray, and we need to pray often.

Learning how to pray is as simple as knowing yourself. Begin with your own needs, your own hurts, and your own desires. Start there. God uses our needs, hurts, and desires, to draw us to Him. Too often, we get so bogged down by all the do's and don'ts of prayer that we never truly pray. We get so preoccupied with how to pray that we forget why we needed to pray in the first place! As a result, the prayer we eventually lift up is a prayer we think God wants to hear, but it is a prayer that doesn't truly reflect our hearts. We find ourselves praying for world peace, missionaries, and the church—things that may not necessarily burden us—while our hearts are raging on the inside with our own personal hurts, cares, and sorrows. The eventual result is that we offer up a prayer full of artificial colorings, preservatives, and yellow #5! It's no wonder so many people find prayer unsatisfying!

If we are to experience satisfying prayer, we need to come to God as we are. He wants to meet the real you. Such an approach is in line with the Gospel of Jesus Christ.

The Gospel frees us to come to God as we are, and not as we hope to be. We need not be afraid to reveal our spiritual warts and shame. We need not be ashamed of our hypocrisy, failures, and shortcomings. This is why Jesus came to this earth. He came to live the perfect life we could not live and die a horrid death we should have died so that we might become His children.

God knows all and He still loves us. This is what makes prayer so enjoyable and satisfying. The Gospel invites the real you to commune with the real God. You can rest in His unconditional love and acceptance, even as you confess sins and desperate needs. The Gospel invites us to offer up a prayer that is completely from our hearts—be it full of sorrows, heartfelt needs, or praise to our Heavenly Father.

PART 3—JOURNALING

Journaling is an essential step to the habit-making process. The exercise of putting pen to paper utilizes areas of your brain that would otherwise remain dormant. As a result, it facilitates the process of transforming a practice into a habit, an exercise into a lifestyle.

Journaling significantly increases the quality and impact of our Scripture reading and prayers. The time and effort that journaling requires is well worth the investment. With regards to Scripture reading, journaling naturally forces us to be more thoughtful in our observations. It protects us from the tendency to quickly skim through a passage without really digesting it. Journaling allows us to think more deeply and wrestle with the text. The very act of writing will deepen the impression of God's Word upon our hearts, and what we learn will not easily be forgotten.

In addition, prayers are noticeably transformed when we journal. It's one thing to internally ask God to forgive you for your selfishness. It's quite another to actually write out and see on paper, "God, forgive me. I am a selfish person." It makes our prayers that much more real and authentic.

Journaling also has the benefit of giving longevity to the lessons you've learned in your life. There are seasons in life where God seems especially close, and what you learn is precious and life-changing. Journaling ensures that such lessons will not be forgotten. I always enjoy picking up an old journal from a few years ago and reading the wonderful lessons that God once taught me. The journal then becomes a testimony of God's faithfulness to you. It acts as a personal, historical record of God's fingerprints on your life.

EXECUTE your plan. To get started, pick several books of the Bible that you want to read and put them in the order you want.

On Days 1 – 12, follow the routine outlined for each day. You can use the journal pages to:
• vent and analyze your feelings
• identify your danger zones
• develop strategies to resist temptations
• brainstorm solutions to challenges
• fine-tune future steps and actions
• note what you have learned about God or yourself

Don't worry about spelling and punctuation—you're the only one who's going to read it!

SUPPORT SYSTEM

Get your family and friends involved. Let them know in advance that you are dedicating a set time alone to spend with God. Ask them to respect your time and support you in your desire to grow closer to the Lord. If you feel you would benefit from a small accountability group that supports and embraces your spiritual growth, an easy way to find one is through your church or pastor.

DEALING WITH FAILURE

We have all broken commitments we've made to ourselves. In your persistence to spend time with the Lord, you may find blemishes on your "perfect record" during the 21 days. When you become dis-tracted or discouraged, try to focus on your victories and forget about your losses. If you miss a day, just keep going until you've finished the 21 day journal. Remember, initiating a ritual is difficult, but maintaining it is not as challenging. My prayer is that by the fourth week, it will become second nature.

VISUALIZE your goal by creating a picture collage of the result of achieving your goal on the following pages. Use photos from magazines or printed off the Internet. Fill in with drawings or photos you take yourself. Start now with a page or two, and add more as you go along.

Examples:
- A photograph of something from God's creation (a natural wonder that captures the majesty and presence of God)
- A prayer that will encourage you in your endeavor
- An inspiring work of art
- A Bible verse that reminds you of what you hope to achieve
- A photograph of loved ones that you hope to impact through your transformed life

Continue to add to your collage and look at it every day. Pictures are powerful motivators—often more powerful than words.

"Before we can begin to see the cross as something done for us,
we have to see it as something done by us."

—John Stott

"Do not be anxious about anything, but in everything by prayer and
supplication with thanksgiving let your requests be made known to God."
—Philippians 4:6

Time spent today:	Scripture read today:

1. Summarize the basic facts of the scripture passage:

_____

_____

_____

_____

2. Meditate on the facts
a. What does this teach me about God?

_____

_____

b. What does God want me to learn about me?

_____

_____

c. Is there a specific sin that I need to repent of?

_____

_____

d. How does this passage testify of who Jesus Christ is and what He has done?

_____

_____

Tip
Consistency is critical! Dedicate the same amount of time or more each day to prayer, at the same time of day.

"Learning to pray doesn't offer us a less busy life; it offers us a less busy heart."

—Paul Miller

3. Respond (confess, praise, express a desire for change)

_____

_____

_____

_____

_____

_____

_____

_____

_____

_____

_____

_____

_____

_____

_____

_____

_____

_____

_____

_____

_____

_____

_____

_____

_____

_____

_____

Today's Thoughts and Prayers

Time spent today:	Scripture read today:

1. Summarize the basic facts of the scripture passage:

_____

_____

_____

_____

2. Meditate on the facts
a. What does this teach me about God?

_____

_____

b. What does God want me to learn about me?

_____

_____

c. Is there a specific sin that I need to repent of?

_____

_____

d. How does this passage testify of who Jesus Christ is and what He has done?

_____

_____

Tip
It's okay to start with a few minutes of prayer each session; just be sure to in-
crease your efforts each day.

"Do not have your concert first, and then tune your instrument afterwards.
Begin the day with the Word of God and prayer, and get first of all into harmony with Him."

—Hudson Taylor

3. Respond (confess, praise, express a desire for change)

Today's Thoughts and Prayers

Time spent today:	Scripture read today:

1. Summarize the basic facts of the scripture passage:

_____

_____

_____

_____

2. Meditate on the facts
a. What does this teach me about God?

_____

_____

b. What does God want me to learn about me?

_____

_____

c. Is there a specific sin that I need to repent of?

_____

_____

d. How does this passage testify of who Jesus Christ is and what He has done?

_____

_____

 Tip
The more you focus on your consistency, the sooner you will experience it.

"...you have made us for yourself,

and our hearts are restless until they find their rest in you."

—Augustine

3. Respond (confess, praise, express a desire for change)

Today's Thoughts and Prayers

Time spent today: Scripture read today:

1. **Summarize** the basic facts of the scripture passage:

2. **Meditate** on the facts
   a. What does this teach me about God?

   b. What does God want me to learn about me?

   c. Is there a specific sin that I need to repent of?

   d. How does this passage testify of who Jesus Christ is and what He has done?

 Tip
Find a friend who shares your goals.

26

"Upon a life I did not live, upon a death I did not die;
another's life, another's death, I stake my whole eternity."

—Horatius Bonar

3. Respond (confess, praise, express a desire for change)

Today's Thoughts and Prayers

Time spent today: **Scripture read today:**

1. Summarize the basic facts of the scripture passage:

2. Meditate on the facts
a. What does this teach me about God?

b. What does God want me to learn about me?

c. Is there a specific sin that I need to repent of?

d. How does this passage testify of who Jesus Christ is and what He has done?

 Tip
While journaling, don't worry about spelling and grammar, write quickly, and don't go back and edit yourself!

"The branch of the vine does not worry, and toil, and rush here to seek for sunshine, and there to find rain. No; it rests in union and communion with the vine; and at the right time, and in the right way, is the right fruit found on it. Let us so abide in the Lord Jesus."

—Hudson Taylor

3. Respond (confess, praise, express a desire for change)

Today's Thoughts and Prayers

Time spent today: **Scripture read today:**

1. **Summarize** the basic facts of the scripture passage:

2. **Meditate** on the facts
   a. What does this teach me about God?

   b. What does God want me to learn about me?

   c. Is there a specific sin that I need to repent of?

   d. How does this passage testify of who Jesus Christ is and what He has done?

 Tip
Be as honest and as thorough as possible in your journaling, and be sure to include your feelings.

"Some people think God does not like to be troubled with our constant coming
and asking. The way to trouble God is not to come at all."

—D.L. Moody

3. Respond (confess, praise, express a desire for change)

Today's Thoughts and Prayers

Time spent today:

Scripture read today:

1. **Summarize** the basic facts of the scripture passage:

2. **Meditate** on the facts
   a. What does this teach me about God?

   b. What does God want me to learn about me?

   c. Is there a specific sin that I need to repent of?

   d. How does this passage testify of who Jesus Christ is and what He has done?

 Tip
Spend time with a Christian brother or sister you respect and admire.

"For a small reward, a man will hurry away on a long journey;
while for eternal life, many will hardly take a single step."

—Thomas a' Kempis

3. Respond (confess, praise, express a desire for change)

Today's Thoughts and Prayers

Congratulations on making it this far! By now, you should be getting into the rhythm of reading, praying, and journaling. What was initially awkward and laborious, is, hopefully, more natural now. You should also be experiencing the benefits of your time with God. Your days should be more reflective and you should find yourself "seeing God" more throughout the day.

If you missed a day or two, don't be overly discouraged and definitely **do not give up!** Jot down the reasons why you missed meeting with God for those days so that you can be more aware of what keeps you from spending time with the Lord. Continue to press on and ask that God will give you the strength and discipline you need to complete this journal.

Also, take this opportunity to assess your progress by answering a few questions:

• Are you on track for attaining your goal within 21 days? If not, why do you think that is and can you do something to get back on track?

• How have you benefited so far in trying to achieve your goal?

• List the habits you have acquired so far.

• What methods have worked best to motivate you?

• What methods did you try that didn't work for you?

• What new methods will you try next?

• What have you learned about yourself so far?

• What have you learned about others so far?

Time spent today:	Scripture read today:

1. **Summarize** the basic facts of the scripture passage:

_____

_____

_____

_____

2. **Meditate** on the facts
   a. What does this teach me about God?

   _____

   _____

   b. What does God want me to learn about me?

   _____

   _____

   c. Is there a specific sin that I need to repent of?

   _____

   _____

   d. How does this passage testify of who Jesus Christ is and what He has done?

   _____

   _____

Tip
Spend time each day imagining how qualitatively different your life will be when God is the anchor.

"The Christian does not think God will love us because we are good,

but that God will make us good because He loves us;

just as the roof of a sunhouse does not attract the sun because it is bright,

but becomes bright because the sun shines on it."

—C.S. Lewis

3. Respond (confess, praise, express a desire for change)

Today's Thoughts and Prayers

Time spent today: Scripture read today:

1. **Summarize** the basic facts of the scripture passage:

   _____

   _____

   _____

   _____

2. **Meditate** on the facts
   a. What does this teach me about God?

   _____

   _____

   b. What does God want me to learn about me?

   _____

   _____

   c. Is there a specific sin that I need to repent of?

   _____

   _____

   d. How does this passage testify of who Jesus Christ is and what He has done?

   _____

   _____

 Tip
Look back at your journal entries so far. Can you spot any patterns of behavior that are interfering with your progress?

"Expect great things from God. Attempt great things for God."

—William Carey

3. Respond (confess, praise, express a desire for change)

_____

_____

_____

_____

_____

_____

_____

_____

_____

_____

_____

_____

_____

_____

_____

_____

_____

_____

_____

_____

_____

_____

_____

_____

_____

Today's Thoughts and Prayers

Time spent today:	Scripture read today:

1. Summarize the basic facts of the scripture passage:

_____

_____

_____

_____

2. Meditate on the facts
a. What does this teach me about God?

_____

_____

b. What does God want me to learn about me?

_____

_____

c. Is there a specific sin that I need to repent of?

_____

_____

d. How does this passage testify of who Jesus Christ is and what He has done?

_____

_____

 Tip
Focus on your victories and let go of your losses.

"The men who have done the most for God in this world have been early on their knees. He who fritters away the early morning, its opportunity and freshness, in other pursuits than seeking God will make poor headway seeking Him the rest of the day. If God is not first in our thoughts and efforts in the morning, He will be in the last place the remainder of the day."

—E.M. Bounds

3. Respond (confess, praise, express a desire for change)

Today's Thoughts and Prayers

Time spent today:	Scripture read today:

1. Summarize the basic facts of the scripture passage:

_____

_____

_____

_____

2. Meditate on the facts
a. What does this teach me about God?

_____

_____

b. What does God want me to learn about me?

_____

_____

c. Is there a specific sin that I need to repent of?

_____

_____

d. How does this passage testify of who Jesus Christ is and what He has done?

_____

_____

 Tip
Avoid negative thinking; meditate on God's grace and His acceptance.

"He is no fool who gives what he cannot keep to gain what he cannot lose."

—Jim Elliot

3. Respond (confess, praise, express a desire for change)

_____

_____

_____

_____

_____

_____

_____

_____

_____

_____

_____

_____

_____

_____

_____

_____

_____

_____

_____

_____

_____

_____

_____

_____

_____

_____

_____

Today's Thoughts and Prayers

Time spent today: Scripture read today:

1. Summarize the basic facts of the scripture passage:

_____

_____

_____

_____

2. Meditate on the facts
   a. What does this teach me about God?

_____

_____

   b. What does God want me to learn about me?

_____

_____

   c. Is there a specific sin that I need to repent of?

_____

_____

   d. How does this passage testify of who Jesus Christ is and what He has done?

_____

_____

Tip
Look back at your journal entries so far. Is there a tactic you used earlier that might help you now?

"My dear Jesus, my Savior, is so deeply written in my heart, that I feel confident,
   that if my heart were to be cut open and chopped to pieces,
      the name of Jesus would be found written on every piece."

—St. Ignatius of Antioch

3. Respond (confess, praise, express a desire for change)

Today's Thoughts and Prayers

Time spent today:	Scripture read today:

1. Summarize the basic facts of the scripture passage:

_____

_____

_____

_____

2. Meditate on the facts
a. What does this teach me about God?

_____

_____

b. What does God want me to learn about me?

_____

_____

c. Is there a specific sin that I need to repent of?

_____

_____

d. How does this passage testify of who Jesus Christ is and what He has done?

_____

_____

Tip
Try to see yourself from someone else's viewpoint. Are you giving your best effort?

"Success is the world's criterion of merit; fidelity is God's."

—Charles Robinson

3. Respond (confess, praise, express a desire for change)

Today's Thoughts and Prayers

Time spent today:

Scripture read today:

1. **Summarize** the basic facts of the scripture passage:

_____

_____

_____

_____

2. **Meditate** on the facts
   a. What does this teach me about God?

   _____

   _____

   b. What does God want me to learn about me?

   _____

   _____

   c. Is there a specific sin that I need to repent of?

   _____

   _____

   d. How does this passage testify of who Jesus Christ is and what He has done?

   _____

   _____

 Tip
Are you discouraged? It might be because you have set unreasonable expectations and goals for yourself. Review your original plan and adjust it as necessary.

"God is most glorified in us when we are most satisfied in Him."

—John Piper

3. Respond (confess, praise, express a desire for change)

Today's Thoughts and Prayers

By now, the "honeymoon" stage may be over and you are finding it increasingly difficult to meet with the Lord. That is to be expected. This is where your commitment and consistency are crucial. You are two-thirds of the way through and only a week away from completing your goal of 21 days of consistency!

A helpful reminder at this point is to remember that reading the Bible and praying is not the *goal* of your devotions. Rather, knowing God is. It is easy to take our eyes off of who we are listening to and who we are talking to since God is someone we cannot see with our physical eyes. Oftentimes, praying and Scripture reading become dutiful when we forget who we are actually communicating with. Remember, we have a personal relationship with **God.** We don't have a relationship with the Bible or prayer itself. The Bible and prayer are only a means to a greater end.

Take this opportunity to assess your progress by answering a few questions:

- Are you on track for attaining your goal within 21 days? If not, why do you think that is and can you do something to get back on track?

- How have you benefited so far in trying to achieve your goal?

- List the habits you have acquired so far.

- What methods have worked best to motivate you?

- What methods did you try that didn't work for you?

- What new methods will you try next?

- What have you learned about yourself so far?

- What have you learned about others so far?

Time spent today:	Scripture read today:

1. Summarize the basic facts of the scripture passage:

2. Meditate on the facts
a. What does this teach me about God?

b. What does God want me to learn about me?

c. Is there a specific sin that I need to repent of?

d. How does this passage testify of who Jesus Christ is and what He has done?

 Tip

You don't want to dwell on the past too much, but consider the hope you feel as you approach your goal in contrast to the heaviness you felt when you were just starting out.

"God whispers to us in our pleasures, speaks in our conscience,
but shouts in our pains: it is His megaphone to rouse a deaf world."

—C.S. Lewis

3. Respond (confess, praise, express a desire for change)

Today's Thoughts and Prayers

Time spent today: | **Scripture read today:**

1. **Summarize** the basic facts of the scripture passage:

_____

_____

_____

_____

2. **Meditate** on the facts
   a. What does this teach me about God?

_____

_____

   b. What does God want me to learn about me?

_____

_____

   c. Is there a specific sin that I need to repent of?

_____

_____

   d. How does this passage testify of who Jesus Christ is and what He has done?

_____

_____

 Tip
Meditate on the changes you've made so far. Praise God for the work He has already begun in you.

"Things do not change; we change."

—Henry David Thoreau

3. Respond (confess, praise, express a desire for change)

_____

_____

_____

_____

_____

_____

_____

_____

_____

_____

_____

_____

_____

_____

_____

_____

_____

_____

_____

_____

_____

_____

_____

_____

_____

_____

_____

_____

Today's Thoughts and Prayers

Time spent today: Scripture read today:

1. **Summarize** the basic facts of the scripture passage:

_____

_____

_____

_____

2. **Meditate** on the facts
   a. What does this teach me about God?

   _____

   _____

   b. What does God want me to learn about me?

   _____

   _____

   c. Is there a specific sin that I need to repent of?

   _____

   _____

   d. How does this passage testify of who Jesus Christ is and what He has done?

   _____

   _____

 Tip
Remove yourself from temptation whenever possible!

"O my Strength, I will sing praises to you, for you,
O God, are my fortress, the God who shows me steadfast love."

—Psalm 59:17

3. Respond (confess, praise, express a desire for change)

Today's Thoughts and Prayers

1. Summarize the basic facts of the scripture passage:

2. Meditate on the facts
a. What does this teach me about God?

b. What does God want me to learn about me?

c. Is there a specific sin that I need to repent of?

d. How does this passage testify of who Jesus Christ is and what He has done?

 Tip
Look back at the picture collages that you have created along the way for encouragement.

"The reason why many fail in battle is because they wait until the hour of battle. The reason why others succeed is because they have gained their victory on their knees long before the battle came...Anticipate your battles; fight them on your knees before temptation comes, and you will always have victory."

—Reuben Archer Torrey

3. Respond (confess, praise, express a desire for change)

_____

_____

_____

_____

_____

_____

_____

_____

_____

_____

_____

_____

_____

_____

_____

_____

_____

_____

_____

_____

_____

_____

_____

_____

Today's Thoughts and Prayers

Time spent today: Scripture read today:

1. **Summarize** the basic facts of the scripture passage:

2. **Meditate** on the facts
   a. What does this teach me about God?

   b. What does God want me to learn about me?

   c. Is there a specific sin that I need to repent of?

   d. How does this passage testify of who Jesus Christ is and what He has done?

 Tip
Press on! By repeating faithful actions you can establish a good habit.

"Your worst days are never so bad that you are beyond the reach of God's grace, nor are your best days ever so good that you are beyond the need of it."

—Jerry Bridges

3. Respond (confess, praise, express a desire for change)

_____

_____

_____

_____

_____

_____

_____

_____

_____

_____

_____

_____

_____

_____

_____

_____

_____

_____

_____

_____

_____

_____

_____

_____

_____

_____

_____

Today's Thoughts and Prayers

Time spent today:	Scripture read today:

1. Summarize the basic facts of the scripture passage:

_____

_____

_____

_____

2. Meditate on the facts
a. What does this teach me about God?

_____

_____

b. What does God want me to learn about me?

_____

_____

c. Is there a specific sin that I need to repent of?

_____

_____

d. How does this passage testify of who Jesus Christ is and what He has done?

_____

_____

 Tip
Tell someone about your journal and how you've changed throughout this process.

"Is prayer your steering wheel or your spare tire?"

—Corrie Ten Boom

3. Respond (confess, praise, express a desire for change)

_____

_____

_____

_____

_____

_____

_____

_____

_____

_____

_____

_____

_____

_____

_____

_____

_____

_____

_____

_____

_____

_____

_____

_____

_____

_____

_____

_____

_____

Today's Thoughts and Prayers

Time spent today: Scripture read today:

1. Summarize the basic facts of the scripture passage:

_____

_____

_____

_____

2. Meditate on the facts
a. What does this teach me about God?

_____

_____

b. What does God want me to learn about me?

_____

_____

c. Is there a specific sin that I need to repent of?

_____

_____

d. How does this passage testify of who Jesus Christ is and what He has done?

_____

_____

 Keep in mind
You're near the end of your journal, but at the inauguration of a transformation in your life.

"Soar back through all your own experiences. Think of how the Lord
has led you in the wilderness and has fed and clothed you every day.
Think of how the Lord's grace has been sufficient for you in all your troubles."

—Charles Spurgeon

3. Respond (confess, praise, express a desire for change)

_____

_____

_____

_____

_____

_____

_____

_____

_____

_____

_____

_____

_____

_____

_____

_____

_____

_____

_____

_____

_____

_____

_____

_____

_____

_____

_____

_____

_____

_____

_____

Today's Thoughts and Prayers

Congratulations on successfully completing the 21 day journal! Whereas it may have felt arduous and stressful to meet with God before, you now probably feel an emptiness if you *don't* meet with Him. Read through your past journal entries as a way to reward yourself! As you see your own progress and development, we hope it encourages you to continue to spend regular time with God.

In addition, for those days that you may have missed, look over the reasons why. Identify any common reasons or factors for your absences, and proactively prepare so that they may not become excuses in the future. You may need to evaluate whether or not an adjustment needs to be made in your scheduling or location.

I do pray that this journal aided you in re-centering your life on Christ. Though spending time with God may not have drastically changed your external circumstances, I am confident that it has changed the way you now respond to life. God bless you as you strive to see with the eyes of faith—through His Word, by prayer, and by journaling. May the Lord continue to weave His story through your life.

FOLLOW-UP by periodically reviewing your goal and your collage. Are you staying true to your original goal? Has this goal changed in any way?

Store the wristband in a place where you'll see it from time to time. You may need to wear it again for a few days!

(You can always use these pages to continue to work your plan if you weren't able to reach your goal in 21 days.)